MORE EASY PIANO TUNES

Anya Suschitzky

Edited by Anthony Marks

Designed and illustrated by Simone Abel

Original music by Anthony Marks and Anya Suschitzky

Arrangements by Anya Suschitzky

Music engraving by Poco Ltd, Letchworth, Herts

This book has lots of tunes for you to play on the piano. They can also be played on the electronic keyboard. As you go through the book the tunes get more difficult and may need more practice. At the end there are some tunes for two people to play.

Throughout the book there are lots of hints on how to improve your playing. There are also facts about different kinds of keyboard instruments and the composers who wrote music for them.

The section called "Music help" on page 62 explains the Italian words, music directions and key signatures used in the book. It also contains hints on practice and suggestions of music to listen to.

Carefree

This tune contains an accidental called C sharp. You can find out more about accidentals below.

Sharps and flats

The sharps and flats at the beginning of a tune are called the key signature. They tell you which notes to play sharp or flat throughout the tune.

A sharp raises a note by a half step or semitone (see page 50).

A flat lowers a note by a half step or semitone.

Accidentals

Sharps, flats and naturals that are not in the key signature are called accidentals. They are added to the staff in front of the note they change.

An accidental only applies to the notes in the bar in which it appears. In the next bar you go back to the original key signature.

To play a sharp or flat you press a black note.

This is C sharp.

When the saints

The first note in the left hand of this tune is a D. It has an extra line of its own.

When a note is higher or lower than the staff, it uses extra lines, called ledger lines. Find out more below.

Ledger lines

To find out which note to play, count up or down from the last note on the staff like this.

5

Lullaby

Lucy Locket

Sliding song

This tune has a few rests in it. You can find out more about rests below.

Rests

This rest lasts as long as a quaver or eighth note*.

This one lasts as long as a crotchet or quarter note*.

This one lasts as long as a minim or half note*.

*These are the names used in North America.

The train is a comin' in

This tune is a spiritual, a kind of American folk song.

You can find out what the time signature of this tune means below.

Time signatures

$\frac{2}{2}$ means there are two minims in each bar. It is sometimes written like this.

$\frac{4}{4}$ means there are four crotchet beats in each bar. It is sometimes written like this.

This time signature tells you there are six quaver beats in each bar.

More about dynamics

Piano (p) tells you to play quietly.

Mezzo forte (mf) tells you to play fairly loudly.

Forte (f) tells you to play loudly.

Singing tune

Adagio means "slowly" (see page 62 for a list of all the Italian words in the book). You can find out about repeat signs below.

This sign is a slur. You play the notes joined by a slur as smoothly as possible (see page 21).

Repeats

These are repeat signs.

When you come to a repeat you go back to the beginning (or the last repeat sign) and play the music once again.

10

Theme from the Trout Quintet

Twinkle, twinkle little star

Moderato means "at a moderate speed".

Cantabile means "with a singing tone".

Words for other speeds

Allegretto means "fairly quickly".

Allegro means "quickly".

12

Minuet

This tune is by the Austrian composer Wolfgang Amadeus Mozart (1756-1791).

The minuet is a dance in ¾ time.

The minuet was very popular in the 17th century, at the court of King Louis XIV of France.

People danced to minuets on the tips of their toes, fairly slowly.

Two by two

A curved line that joins two notes of the same pitch* is called a tie. To play tied notes press the key for the first note, and hold it until the end of the second note.

A dot after a note or rest means it lasts for half its length again.

* The pitch of a note is how high or low it is.

Warming up

Playing this tune will help your fingers warm up so that they work better when you play tunes.

Try to play this tune as smoothly as possible. Playing smoothly is called *legato* (see page 21).

Getting strong

This tune will help you to strengthen your fingers.

Play it slowly at first, and increase your speed gradually.

March

English minuet

This tune is by the English composer Croft (1678-1727).

You can find out what *rit.* means below.

Rit. is short for *ritenuto*, which means "slow down".

Cradle song

Using the sustaining pedal*

On the piano, the pedal on the right is called the sustaining pedal. It helps you move smoothly between two notes or chords. When you press it, the notes you have played will continue to sound. This is called sustaining. You can then move to the next note without making a break in the music.

* You can find out more about the sustaining pedal on page 45.

Minuet

This tune is by the French composer Rameau (1683-1764).

It was written for the harpsichord. You can find out more about the harpsichord on page 29.

Allegretto

Minuet

This tune was written by
Leopold Mozart. He was
the father of Wolfgang
Amadeus Mozart, who
wrote the tunes on pages
13, 34 and 52.

This is a triplet. It
tells you to fit three
notes into one beat.

Hymn tune

Try to play this tune smoothly. This is called *legato*.

You can find out more below.

Playing legato

To play legato, you keep your finger down on one key until you press the key for the next note.

It helps if you keep your fingers close to the keyboard when you are playing legato.

The happy hare

This sign is a pause. You hold the note with the pause above it for about half its length again.

There is a special kind of repeat in this tune. Find out more below.

First-time bars and second-time bars

The first time through, you play the first-time bar.

When you repeat, leave out the first-time bar and play the second-time bar instead.

Then continue with the rest of the tune.

Burlesque

This tune is by Leopold Mozart.

A burlesque is a comical tune.

Try, try, try again

This is a *staccato* note. Play notes like this as short as possible.

This is an accented note. Notes with accents sound louder and more important than other notes. You can find out more below.

Accents and staccatos

To play notes with accents and staccatos, you press the keys a bit harder and more quickly than usual.

If you are playing a staccato note, you should also lift your finger as soon as possible, and make a break before the next note.

Lilliburlero

This is a famous Irish folk tune.

Fanfare

A fanfare is a short piece which is often played on trumpets. Fanfares are used for processions and celebrations of important people.

Maestoso means "grandly".

Liza Jane

This tune is an American folk song.

Moderato

mf

Listening to piano music

Most famous composers have written music for the piano or earlier keyboard instruments such as the harpsichord. You can find recordings of many of these pieces in the library or record shop. Mozart (1756-1791) wrote lots of sonatas and concertos for the piano. Try listening to piano concertos no.25 and no.27.

Bach (1685-1750) wrote music for the harpsichord (see page 29), the organ (see page 47), and the clavichord (an early form of the piano). Some of this music can be played on the piano. Try listening to *The Well-Tempered Clavier* and the *Goldberg Variations*. You can find out more about piano music on page 32.

A piano concerto is for a piano and orchestra. A piano sonata is for a piano alone.

Happy march

poco a poco diminuendo

28

The conquering hero

This tune is by Handel (1685-1759). It is from his oratorio *Judas Maccabeus*. An oratorio is a piece for a choir and an orchestra on a religious subject.

D.C. al Fine means you go back to the beginning and play the music again. Stop when you reach the word *Fine*.

The harpsichord and the piano

The first harpsichords were built about five hundred years ago. The notes of a harpsichord are fairly quiet. Each key is linked to a piece of feather quill or plastic called a plectrum. When the keys are pressed, the plectrums pluck the strings.

When pianos were developed in the early 18th century, they became more popular than harpsichords. This is because they could play louder and longer notes than harpsichords, and because it was possible to vary the way the notes sounded.

The last rose of summer

This is an Irish folk song.

On the little hearth

This lullaby was first sung by European Jews on their way to the USA. Look out for the first- and second-time bars (see page 22).

Lullaby

Listening to piano music

During the 19th century, the piano became very popular. Composers such as Beethoven, Schubert, Schumann, Chopin and Liszt wrote lots of difficult music which was played in concerts by very good pianists called "virtuosi". Some also wrote shorter, more simple pieces for people to play at home. Schubert, who composed the tune on this page, wrote many piano sonatas and shorter pieces for piano such as *Impromptus*, *Moments musicaux*, and waltzes. He also wrote over 600 songs for voice and piano called *Lieder*, many of which have very good piano parts.

Smooth snakes

Chords and arpeggios

The tune on this page contains arpeggios in the left hand part. Arpeggios are the notes of a chord which are spread out so that you play one at a time, either from the bottom up or from the top down. You can find out more about arpeggios and the scales that go with them on pages 50-51.

Sometimes chords are arranged to form a pattern called an alberti bass, in which the bottom note of the chord is played first, then the top note, then the middle note, and then the top note again. The alberti bass is named after Domenico Alberti, who often wrote bass lines like this.

Là ci darem la mano

This tune comes from Mozart's opera *Don Giovanni*, which is based on an old Spanish story.

It is a sung by a man called Don Giovanni and a woman called Zerlina.

D.C. al Fine

Fingerings

The pieces in this book tell you which fingers to use. This helps you to place your hand in a position where you will be able to play all the notes. Many of the fingerings tell you to tuck your thumb under your hand. This helps you to change the position of your hand. Playing scales and arpeggios (see pages 50-51) will also help you to tuck your thumb under your hand.

Minuet

This tune is by the German composer Bach (1685-1750), who came from a large family of musicians.

Bach wrote lots of music for the clavichord, the harpsichord and the organ. You can find out more about his music on page 27.

Allegretto

35

Theme from Beethoven's Violin Concerto

This tune is by Beethoven. Near the end, the left hand part is written in the treble clef.

A violin concerto is for a violin and an orchestra. This tune comes from the last movement (section) of Beethoven's concerto.

Air

This tune is by the
English composer
Purcell (1659-1695).

Listening to piano music

On the next page there is some music by the German composer Schumann (1810-1856). Schumann was also a piano player and a writer on music. You could listen to his Piano Concerto in A minor, and to his pieces for solo piano such as *Papillons* and *Carnaval*. He also wrote some less difficult music called *Album for the Young*. The pieces on pages 38, 44 and 56 of this book are from *Album for the Young*.

Humming song

This piece is by Schumann. It is from *Album for the Young*.

Play this tune very smoothly.

When you see a note written as a quaver and a crotchet at the same time, hold the crotchet down for its full value, but keep the quaver line going as well.

This is another way of making you emphasize notes.

Make sure you play the
notes of the left hand line
in the correct clef. They
are in the treble clef at the
beginning, but the clef
changes twice during the
piece.

Musette

This tune is by Bach. It is from a group of dances called a suite.

This tune has a continuous note in the left hand called a drone. It imitates an old instrument called a musette, which was like bagpipes.

Moderato

40

Greensleeves

This is an old English tune. It is also known as *The Blacksmith*. The time signature means there are six crotchets in a bar.

Pipe and drum

There is a change of key signature and time signature in this tune. You can find out more below.

Pesante means "heavily".

Changes of time and key signature

Sometimes the time signature changes in the middle of a piece. In this tune it changes from four to three quavers in a bar. It will be easier to change time signature if you count the quaver beats in your head. This is because the speed of the quavers remains the same throughout the piece.

The key signature of a piece can also change. When this happens, a new key signature cancels the old one. In this tune, play F sharps before, and B flats after the change.

Blue study

Tenuto marks

Melody

Interpretation

Every performance of a piece of music is different. This is because there are many small changes you can make to alter the way the music sounds. You can play the music staccato, legato or a little faster, slower, louder or softer.

During your practice, try different ways of playing each phrase until you like the way it sounds. This is called interpretation. Interpretation gives your playing its own special character.

Schumann was married to a pianist and composer called Clara Wieck.

She knew many famous musicians, including Brahms (1833-1897).

More about the sustaining pedal

Sometimes you can use the sustaining pedal even if it is not marked in the music.

You can use the pedal to play big jumps more smoothly.

Make sure that when you use the pedal, you only press it very gently.

Paris Quartet

This tune is by the German composer Telemann (1681-1767).

This sign is a trill. You can find out how to play trills below.

Trills

To play a trill, you play the note on which the trill is written and the note above it (see below).

Alternate between the two notes for as long as the note with the trill on it lasts, like this.

Chorale

This tune is by Bach. It was written for the organ. You can find out more about the organ below.

Chorales can be sung too.

Adagio

f

The organ

The organ is the oldest kind of keyboard instrument. Its sound is produced by pipes of different sizes, made from metal and wood.

Bach was a famous organ player. He wrote lots of music for the organ. Some of it can be played on the piano.

Minuet

This tune is by Bach. It is from a collection of music he wrote for his wife Anna Magdalena.

The little notes in bar six are called grace notes. Find out how to play them below.

Grace notes

Grace notes decorate the music. Usually you play them just before the beat.

Don't play them too quickly.

48

Summer song

This tune has another kind of decoration called an *acciaccatura* ("a-chak-a-too-ra").

You can find out more about acciaccaturas below.

Acciaccaturas

The word acciaccatura comes from an Italian word meaning "to crush".

You play an acciaccatura as quickly as possible, before the note to which it is attached.

Scales and arpeggios

Scales are chains of notes that go up and down by step. There are two kinds of step in a scale: whole steps (tones) and half steps (semitones). A tone is made of two semitones put together. There are several kinds of scale. One of the most common is the major scale. The order of the tones and semitones in every major scale is the same. The steps between the third and fourth notes, and the seventh and eighth notes in a major scale are semitones. All the other steps are tones.

SEMITONE
TONE
TONE
TONE
SEMITONE
TONE
TONE

Here is a major scale. It starts on C and is in the key of C major. Use the music below to play C major.

Here is another way of playing a C major scale, in which your hands move in opposite directions. This is called contrary motion.

Before you play tunes you can warm up with a few scales.

Arpeggios are spread chords. You can play them at the beginning of your practice, with the scale of the same key. The notes of an arpeggio are the first, third, fifth and the eighth notes of the scale in the same key.

Here is the arpeggio of C major.

Scales and arpeggios of more than one octave

The scales on page 50 are one octave long. An octave is the distance between one note and the next note above or below it with the same name.

When you play scales and arpeggios, repeat them a few times by starting at the bottom of the piano and moving up through several octaves.

To play scales and arpeggios of more than one octave long, you need to change the fingering at the end of the first octave.

Below, you can play the scale and arpeggio of G major. Both of them are two octaves long.

Many of the pieces on the next pages contain parts that are based on scales and arpeggios.

Rondo

In a rondo, the first tune you hear comes back several times during the piece, with new tunes in between.

This tune is by Mozart.

Allegro

52

The left hand plays in the treble clef at the beginning of this tune.

The groups of semiquavers will become easier if you play them slowly at first.

53

Waltz

This tune is by the Russian composer Tchaikovsky (1840-1893). There are E sharps in the third line. E sharp is the same as F natural.

The waltz is a German dance in $\frac{3}{4}$ time. It was popular in the 19th century.

Song of the reapers

This tune is by Schumann.

It contains acciaccaturas (see page 49). Play them just before the main beat.

Polonaise

This tune is by Bach. It is from the book of music he wrote for his wife Anna Magdalena.

The polonaise was first danced in Poland during parades and processions.

In this tune you could try playing the quavers in the right hand part staccato, and the semiquavers legato.

My vineyard (part B)

This tune is a duet (a piece for two people). It is based on a Russian folk tune.

Part B is played by the person at the lower end of the piano. Part A is played by the person at the top end of the piano.

Allegro

58

My vineyard
(part A)

It helps if you count
a bar together
before you start.

When you play duets,
listen to the other
person so that you
play together exactly
in time.

Humoresque
(part B)

This duet is by the Czech composer Dvořák (1841-1904).

Poco lento e grazioso means "quite slowly and gracefully". *Leggiero* means "lightly".

60

Humoresque
(part A)

A humoresque is a lively, but also slightly sad tune.

Dvořák wrote eight humoresques for piano.

Music help

Italian terms

This list explains the Italian words used in the book.

adagio – slowly
allegretto – fairly quickly
allegro – quickly
andante – at a walking pace
cantabile – singing
crescendo (cresc.) – getting
  louder
D.C. al Fine – back to the
beginning, to *Fine*
diminuendo (dim.) –

getting softer
forte (f) – loudly
grazioso – gracefully
largo – slowly and stately
legato – smoothly
leggiero – lightly
maestoso – grandly
mezzo forte (mf) – fairly
  loudly
mezzo piano (mp) – fairly

quietly
moderato – at a moderate
  speed
pesante – heavily
piano (p) – quietly
poco a poco – little by little
poco lento – fairly slowly
ritenuto (rit.) – held back
staccato – short
tenuto – held

Key signatures

The key signature of a tune tells you which notes to play sharp or flat. Here are some of the key signatures used in the book.

C major

G major

D major

F major

B♭ major

Practice

At the beginning of your practice, you should warm up with some scales, arpeggios and exercises. If you come across any difficult bars when you play tunes, try them slowly. You could also invent exercises to help you with the difficult bars, such as playing them with a new rhythm or with staccato and then legato phrasing. When you go back to the original music it will seem easier, and then you can gradually increase your speed.

When you play, always choose a speed that you can manage without making too many mistakes. As you get to know the music you will be able to play faster if you want to.

More music to listen to

Here is a list of music for piano that you might enjoy listening to.
Bach: *Goldberg Variations*
Mozart: Piano Concerto no.19
Beethoven: *Emperor Concerto*
Schubert: *Fantasia in F minor for two
  pianos*
Mendelssohn: *Songs without words*
Schumann: Piano Concerto in A minor
Chopin: *Preludes, Nocturnes*
Liszt: *Hungarian Rhapsodies*
Brahms: Piano Trio in B major
Mussorgsky: *Pictures at an Exhibition*
Tchaikovsky: Piano Concerto no.1

Grieg: Piano Concerto in A minor
Debussy: *Preludes*
Rachmaninov: Piano Concerto no.2
Ravel: *Concerto for the Left Hand*
Bartók: Piano Concerto no.2
Prokofiev: Piano Concerto no.2
Gershwin: *Rhapsody in Blue*
Shostakovich: Piano Concerto no.1

Many jazz musicians play the piano. You could listen to Scott Joplin, Duke Ellington, Fats Waller, Charles Mingus, Oscar Peterson and Herbie Hancock.

Index of tunes

Index